Clouds That Look Like Things

Clouds That Look Like Things

Photographed by members of The Cloud Appreciation Society

Edited, designed and written by Gavin Pretor-Pinney, society founder
with assistance from Ian Loxley, society gallery editor
www.cloudappreciationsociety.org

SCEPTRE

First published in Great Britain in 2012 by Sceptre
An imprint of Hodder & Stoughton, An Hachette UK company

1

Printed and bound in China by C&C Offset Printing Co. Ltd
A CIP catalogue record for this title is available from the British Library
ISBN 9781444728286

Designed and typeset by Gavin Pretor-Pinney

Hodder & Stoughton policy is to use papers that are natural, renewable and recyclable
products and made from wood grown in sustainable forests. The logging and
manufacturing processes are expected to conform to the environmental regulations of the
country of origin.

Hodder & Stoughton Ltd
338 Euston Road
London NW1 3BH

www.sceptrebooks.com

Contents

Introduction 7

Airborne Animals 11

Outdoor Pursuits 37

When Clouds have Bad-hair Days 53

Familiar Faces 61

Weird and Wonderful 75

What Exactly are Clouds? 100

The Official Classifications 106

Acknowledgements 108

Index of Photographers 109

Captions Index 110

Introduction

Is it a bird? Is it a plane? No, it's a ghost carrying the shopping. Or a pink elephant. Or an enormous pair of Mick Jagger lips. At The Cloud Appreciation Society, we love finding shapes in the clouds. It's what lazy afternoons in the park were made for and we think everyone should do more of it.

This is why we've always encouraged members of The Cloud Appreciation Society to email us their photographs of clouds that look like things, which we put up on our ever-expanding online gallery. In 2007, we compiled a little book of twenty-eight of these photographs, which we called *A Pig With Six Legs and Other Clouds*. Over the four years since then, not only has our membership swelled from 8,000 to 28,000, the Society's collection of clouds that look like things has grown to over a thousand images. Dinosaurs, dragons, flying saucers... You name it, we've got it – so long as it's made of tiny water particles suspended in the lower atmosphere.

With such a wealth of fantastic 'cloud lookalikes' to choose from, it seemed high time for another book of clouds that look like things, bigger and better than the last. The photographs in this new collection are not only more plentiful – there are a total of eighty-six of them – but they are also larger in format. I also realised that this time around I had the opportunity to include an explanation of why we get clouds at all. If you want to know what causes these strange and amusing cloud shapes to appear in the first place, have a look at the section 'What Exactly are Clouds?' on p100.

No other organisation could have come up with a set of images like these. In order to take a picture of a cloud in the shape of tennis pro Andy Murray as he is serving an ace over the west coast of Scotland, you have to be in the right place at the right time, with a camera to hand and, crucially, you have to be the sort of person to let your imagination run free. Some are better at this than others but even the best cloudspotters will find that fantastic cloud shapes just don't appear that often. This is why you need a worldwide network of cloudspotters to collect them. And that is exactly what we have with The Cloud Appreciation Society: an international group of people who live with their heads in the clouds and their cameras in their pockets.

Finding shapes in the clouds is something we all did when we were young and for this reason it is the most inclusive form of cloudspotting. Perhaps because it reminds us of carefree days in our youth, it is also the most lighthearted and relaxing kind. No great concentration is needed to notice that the cloud above you looks like a heart. In fact, it is easier to see cloud shapes when you aren't trying too hard. Nor do you need to know your Cumulus from your Altostratus to see that the one over there looks like a flying saucer. But if you are interested in knowing the proper, scientific names of the clouds in these photographs, these are all listed in 'The Official Classifications' on p106.

Sadly, one question always comes up when people see images like these: have they been manipulated in Photoshop? This is something that we take very seriously at The Cloud Appreciation Society. We ruthlessly reject any fiddling with images other than some simple contrast and brightness correction. Whenever possible, we choose images where the photographer took several shots as the cloud developed so that we can be confident that there was no image manipulation. As a result, we feel satisfied that all the clouds in this book are free from funny business and appear just as the winds created them.

We are extremely grateful to all The Cloud Appreciation Society members who have so generously agreed to their images being reproduced in this book. Their photographic skills and, more importantly, their sky awareness and vivid imaginations are what have made *Clouds That Look Like Things* a cloudspotting *tour de force*.

Finding cloud shapes is the perfect antidote to modern life. One reason is because it is a pointless activity: it achieves absolutely nothing. Such aimless pleasures are more important today than they have ever been. The modern world contrives to make us feel guilty unless we are constantly busy. When we're not studying or working, we must be maintaining our Twitter feeds and changing our Facebook status updates, while posting YouTube videos of ourselves as we do so. We need excuses to do nothing. And what better excuse than looking for a cloud in the shape of an enormous rat telling a secret? Or a goggle-eyed flying saucer? Or Sherlock Holmes smoking his pipe as he gazes off towards the setting sun?

Gavin Pretor-Pinney
Founder of The Cloud Appreciation Society
November 2011
cloudappreciationsociety.org

Airborne Animals

A baby elephant over Bedford, Bedfordshire, UK.
Ian Forsdike, Member 16,289.

A mummy elephant over Terschelling, The Netherlands.
Saskia van der Sluis, Member 23,801.

A dolphin leaping over Sausalito, California, US.
David R Holbrooke, Member 22,251.

A shark patrolling the road from Marrakesh to Agadir, Morocco.
Ellen Claire Ward, Member 15,611.

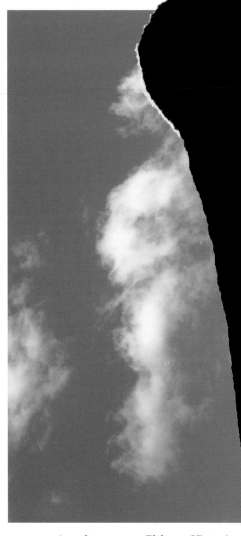

A rainbow fish caught in a net over Elgin, Moray, Scotland.
Alan C Tough, Member 21,958.

A seahorse over Eltham, Victoria, *A*
Jordie Albiston, Member 4,262, spotted by

A sunfish over Big Bend National Park, Texas, US.
Barry Milyovsky, Member 17,394.

A giant eel over Ouaisné Bay, St Brelade, Jersey, UK.
Frank Le Blancq, Member 7,914.

A red snapper over The Blasket Islands, County Kerry, Ireland.
Gavin Tobin, Member 23,454.

A bird of paradise (within iridescent nacreous clouds) over Leeds, UK.
Lee Montgomerie, Member 280.

A cockerel on the roof and in the sky over Bishop, California, US.
Andrew Kirk, Member 6,333.

A baby Tyrannosaurus Rex over Orkney, Scotland...
Rebecca Marr, Member 7,548.

...and the grown-up version over Friesland, The Netherlands.
Megan L Anderson, Member 22,429.

A bee hovering in the shadows over Elgin, Moray, Scotland.
Alan C Tough, Member 21,958.

A rabbit over Friesland, The Netherlands, looking up...
Maartje and Owain Murphy, Members 27,209 & 28,116.

...as a horse takes a flying leap over Hyde, Cheshire, UK.
Jeanne Dixon-Rowland, Member 16,274.

A fat bunny doing gymnastics over Modena, Italy.
Fiorella Iacono, Member 9,702.

A pig's head over Finchley, North London, UK.
Nikki Lofting, Member 28,063.

A giant rat over Tortona, Alessandria, Italy, telling a secret...
Pietro Cordelli, Member 16,468.

...to a gorilla and a hippopotamus over Stockgrove Country Park, Leighton Buzzard, UK.
Jeremy Williams, Member 28,064.

A suicidal Afghan Hound over Wigmore, Herefordshire, UK, contemplating the end...
Howard Kirby, Member 2,163.

...as a wolf howls 'Don't jump!' over Winter Hill, Bolton, UK.
Gareth Fairclough, Member 21,379.

A polar bear in shades taking a stroll along Bamburgh Beach, Northumberland, UK.
Bill Williamson, Member 17,078.

A puppy begging for dinner over Manchester, UK.
Phil Leyland, Member 20,114.

A swan swimming over Colorado Springs, Colorado, US...
Gail J Harrison, Member 17,912.

...and taking off over Upton, Lincolnshire, UK.
Ian Loxley, Member 1,868.

Outdoor Pursuits

A surfer kneeling on the board over Sabden, Lancashire, UK.
Elizabeth Hart, Member 12,457.

A swimmer waving from out in the surf over Malltraeth, Anglesey, UK.
John Rowlands, Member 9,641.

A frisbee thrower over Banff, Alberta, Canada.
John A Adam, Member 6,347.

A topless sunbather over Wooler, Northumberland, UK.
Sue Shaw, Member 23,526.

Boxing practice in the park over Weed, California, US.
Patricia Matthews, Member 9,722.

 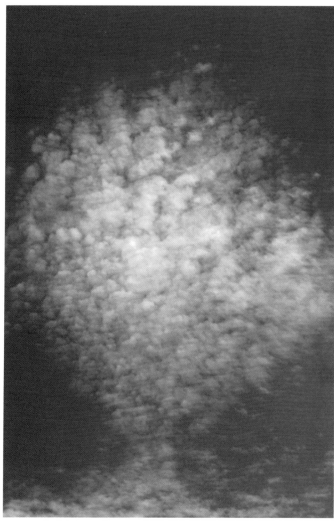

Lovers over Zurich, Switzerland, having a cuddle...
Danièle Siebenhaar, Member 12,650.

...beneath a tree over Bexhill-on-Sea, East Sussex, UK.
Alan Thomassen, Member 26,381.

An angry neighbour over Catcott, Somerset, UK, shouts across the fence...
Ron Westmaas, Member 4,451.

...at Lightning Boy who's climbing on the wires again over Bangkok, Thailand.
Alex Cliff, Member 28,073.

Outdoor Pursuits

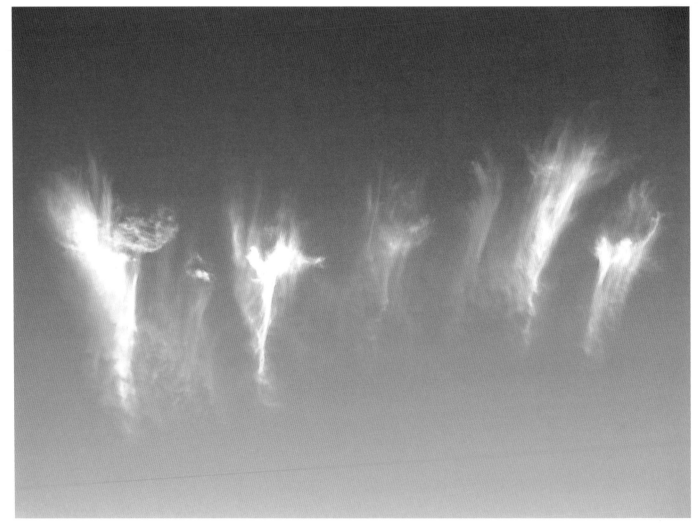

Ballet dancers warming up over Burton Bradstock, Dorset, UK.
Paul Loebig, Member 15,045.

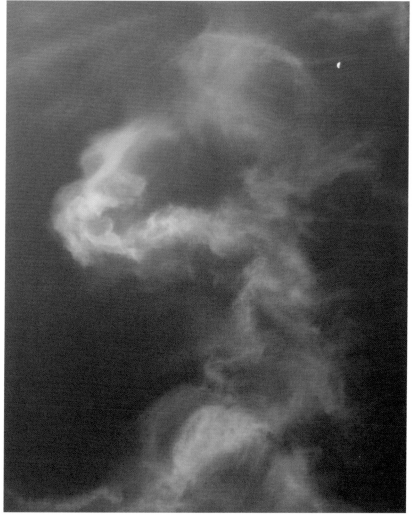

A bodybuilder flexing his muscles over Pacifica, California, US.
Paul A Jones, Member 18,562.

Rowers over South Leigh, Oxfordshire, UK, take to the river...
Marie Dent, Member 9,934.

...but watch out for the waterfall over Geneva, Switzerland!
Gianni Cerutti, Member 17,232 .

'Hang gliders, turn right here' over Melbourne, Australia.
Rowena Coutts, Member 28,177.

An air guitar performance over Isle of Harris, Scotland.
Donald Macleod Hodgson, Member 14,293.

A thumbs up over Istanbul, Turkey.
Lazaros Filippidis, Member 28,077.

When Clouds have Bad-hair Days

A bad-hair day over Cullen, Moray, Scotland.
Moragh McDonald, Member 14,912.

A bad-hair day over Boston, Lincolnshire, UK.
Jane Desforges, Member 12,471.

A bad-hair day over Montpellier, France.
Julien Mekhneche, Member 20,796.

A comb-over bad-hair day over Pori, Finland.
Tiina Huhtakangas, Member 26,809.

A big-bad-hair day over Newton-on-Ouse, North Yorkshire, UK, taken in the 1950s.
The late Gordon Wright, father of Richard Wright, Member 16,728.

A bad-hair-and-big-nose day over Upton, Lincolnshire, UK.
Ian Loxley, Member 1,868.

Santa having a bad-hair day over St Ives, Cornwall, UK.
Mandy Millie Flockton, Member 26,440.

Familiar Faces

The film director Alfred Hitchcock watching a storm over Ecclefechan, Scotland.
Anne Downie, Member 12,153.

Andy Murray serving an ace over Traigh Beach, Arisaig, Scotland.
Peter Rowell, Member 21,546.

The musketeer Aramis over Ann Arbor, Michigan, US.
Thomas J Bethell, Member 23,594.

The musketeer d'Artagnan over Erm, The Netherlands.
Nienke Lantman, Member 24,009.

The musketeer Athos over Loudonville, Ohio, US, is frustrated to have lost his feathered hat...
Catherine Strong Wilson, Member 16,752.

...Oh, there it is over Mount Shasta, California, US.
Patricia Matthews, Member 9,722.

Hamlet with Yorick's skull over South Yearle, Northumberland, UK.
Sue Shaw, Member 23,526.

Jesus over Christchurch, New Zealand.
Gregory Dowson, Member 15,705.

Mick Jagger's lips over Sherwood Rise, Nottingham, UK.
Peter Beardsley, Member 18,862.

Sherlock Holmes over Kalkan, Turkey.
Michael Menger, Member 16,382.

Homer Simpson befriends a squirrel over Cardiff, South Wales, UK.
Zan Light, Member 21,274.

One of those grumpy old men from The Muppet Show over Bangkok, Thailand.
Alex Cliff, Member 28,073.

Weird and Wonderful

'FIVE' over Vienna, Austria...
Klaus Nüchtern, Member 13,220.

...'FOUR' over Welling, Kent, UK...
Carolyn Johannesen, Member 21,124.

...'THREE' over Naples, Italy...
Modestino Carbone, Member 7,416.

...'TWO' over Drumnadrochit, Inverness, Scotland...
Laurence Tondelier, Member 16,549.

...'ONE' over Mercogliano, Italy...
Modestino Carbone, Member 7,416.

...'Cleared for takeoff' over Norwich, Norfolk, UK...
Doug Taylor, Member 16,924.

...'Oops!' Over Houston, Texas, US...
Jason Tack, Member 7,413.

...'Oh no!' Over the Matterhorn, on the Italian-Swiss border.
Andrew Solomon, Member 25,064.

The mother-in-law's gone and left her wedding hat on top of Lion's Head mountain, Cape Town, South Africa...
Mary Hemsworth, Member 17,408.

...and her walking stick over Naas, County Kildare, Ireland.
Melissa de Robeck, Member 9,668.

A giant sniffing a row of herbs over Grou, Friesland, The Netherlands.
Keimpe Bleeker, Member 11,484.

A ghost carrying home the shopping over Aberdeen, Scotland.
Mark Murray, Member 12,328.

A smoking chimney over Munich, Germany.
Bernhard Kaliner, Member 9,964.

A goggle-eyed UFO over the Devils Marbles, Northern Territory, Australia.
Cobalt Osanga, Member 17,067.

A Harry Potter scar over Bishop, California, US.
Eric Beyne, Member 25,009.

A quill over Jamieson, Victoria, Australia.
Cathryn Tremain, Member 12,276.

'You are here' over Milford Sound, New Zealand…
John Gray, Member 20,435.

...'Or are you?' over Steinenbronn, Germany.
Michael Kehl, Member 7,703.

A dragon landing on the Isle of Skye, Scotland.
Jules Janes, Member 25,419.

A witch taking off over Marsiling, Singapore.
Tracey Yap, Member 23,656.

'Talk to the hand' over Chadbury, Worcestershire, UK...
Steve Gledhill, Member 11,330.

'...'cause the face ain't listening!' over Porthcawl, Wales, UK.
Karen M Lloyd, Member 17,664.

A broken heart over Montpellier, France.
Julien Mekhneche, Member 20,796.

A mended heart over Sedona, Arizona, US.
Adele Good, Member 14,461.

What Exactly are Clouds?

What are they made of?

This one's simple: they're made of water. Low clouds, like the rabbit on p25, are made up of tiny water droplets; each one might be no larger than half the width of this full stop. High clouds, such as the bodybuilder on p47, are made of ice – little crystals of the stuff, which are often in the shape of six-armed stars or six-sided plates or columns. Mid-level clouds are sometimes made of droplets, sometimes crystals, sometimes a mixture of the two. It is hard to say which. They like to keep us guessing.

Why do we have them?

Because there is a lot of water around – water covers about 80% of the surface of our planet if you include ice – and it behaves in a very unusual way. It is the only substance we find on Earth in solid, liquid and gas forms. Nothing else exists in all three states within the temperatures and pressures typical of our atmosphere. Our cloudscapes are so rich and varied because of the abundance of water and the ease with which it changes from one state to another.

We are all used to liquid and solid water (ice), so it is not too hard to think of clouds being made up of lots of little bits of them. Much less familiar is the idea of water in the form of a gas. But there is plenty of that around us. It is called 'water vapour', and is one of the many gases that make

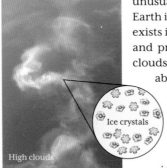

Water droplets

Low clouds

High clouds

Ice crystals

Whether clouds are made of water droplets, ice crystals or a combination or the two depends largely on the air temperature, which varies with altitude.

up the air we breathe. It can get swept up in the air by evaporating from oceans, lakes, ponds, and wet or snowy ground, and by being sweated off the leaves of plants trying to stay cool (a process known as 'transpiration').

When water is being a gas, its molecules are far apart, flying around individually, jostling with the molecules of the other gases that make up our air. Each molecule is far too small to see so water vapour is invisible. Therefore, when the water in the air above us is in gas form, the sky looks clear to us. Only when a few thousand million of the water molecules stick together to form a liquid droplet or an ice crystal is there a chance of us seeing it.

We don't always see water as cloud. If the droplets are too small and scarce, they might appear as a slight haze or be noticeable only if they catch the sunlight enough to reveal shafts of light and shadow, like those showing in the cloud-free region below the sunset face on p97. But when they're large and plentiful enough, they can appear as a bright white cloud, like the mended heart on p99.

Why are some white, some grey and some coloured?

Since clouds are made of water, you might wonder why they aren't see-through – like a glass of water or a clear sliver of ice. This is because the water is in the form of countless tiny particles, rather than one large chunk. The surfaces of all these droplets or crystals reflect and bend the sunlight this way and that. Whenever we see sunlight shining off something that scatters it randomly, we tend to see it as white. This is why the foam of a breaking wave or a layer of snow looks white. The surfaces of the bubbles in the wave and the crystals of the snow scatter the sunlight in all directions, and this we see as white.

A cloud doesn't look like this.

But not all clouds are white. Sometimes they look grey, at others orange or red. Occasionally, clouds can even appear as multi-coloured, like the bird of paradise on p20.

The greyness depends greatly on the background. The same cloud can look grey when it's seen against a bright background, such as the broken heart on p98, and white when it's seen against a darker one, like Andy Murray serving an ace on p63. In other words, the shade is partly owing to how our brains compare the brightness of different parts of a scene. Another factor is whether the side of the cloud that is facing you is lit by the Sun, like the angry neighbour on p44, or is in shadow, like the pig's head on p27. The darkness of the side in shadow depends on how thick the cloud is and how densely packed are its water particles. The more droplets or ice crystals there are between the sunny and shaded sides, the more the sunlight entering the cloud is dispersed before it emerges from the other side. This is why the sky looks dark grey just before a heavy shower. A cloud has to grow very tall to produce a heavy downpour, so less sunlight emerges from its base than is the case in other parts of the sky.

And what about colours? Rosy-coloured clouds, such as the red snapper on p19, are the result of being lit by the Sun as it is rising or setting. Out of the spectrum that makes up sunlight, the blue-looking light tends to be scattered more than the rest by the gases of our atmosphere. So at the beginning and end of the day when the light has passed through a lot of the atmosphere to reach us, compared to in the middle of the day, more of the blue constituents have been knocked out, leaving an abundance of the red, orange and yellow looking light.

The multi-coloured clouds are caused by something completely different. It is an effect known as 'diffraction' – the name for the way sunlight bends as it passes around a cloud's tiny particles. The colours that make up sunlight bend by varying amounts so can be separated by diffraction. When the droplets or crystals are particularly small and all about the same size, the diffracted sunlight appears as beautiful bands of colour. This is known as 'iridescence', and resembles the mother-of-pearl colours you see inside an oyster shell. The rainbow fish on p16 is another example of this.

How do clouds form?

If clouds appear when the water in the air changes from invisible water vapour to visible particles, what causes the change to happen?

The air becoming colder, that's what.

When air cools, its molecules fly around more slowly. Droplets or ice crystals form when the molecules have slowed so much that they start sticking together in tiny clumps, which we see as clouds.

Most often this happens when air rises. Why? Because when air rises it expands and whenever gases expand they become colder. It's why the nozzle of a spray-can becomes cold as the gas within expands upon rushing out.

A region of air in our atmosphere can rise for many reasons. On a sunny day, the air just above a patch of sun-warmed ground becomes hotter than the air elsewhere so it expands and starts to float upwards. This column of air cools as it rises, and is called a 'thermal'. If the air cools enough for some of its water vapour to form into droplets, a Cumulus cloud appears, like the kneeling surfer on p38. The same can happen to the air heated over a warm ocean current, or when warm air blows beneath a region of cold air so that pockets of the lighter air float up through the heavier, colder air above. This is what causes a layer of cloud clumps like those that make up the tree on p43.

Another way that air rises and cools to form clouds is when it has to pass over an obstacle, such as a hill or mountain. This is why you often see clouds around the tops of mountains. The mother-in-law's wedding hat on p84 is a particularly dramatic example of this. It is also why you sometimes see clouds appearing downwind of a mountain peak. Known as lenticular clouds, and shaped like discs, these often look like the flying saucer on the front cover.

Extended layers of cloud form when a large region of air, which might be spread over many hundreds of square miles, rises *en masse* as it collides with a region of differing air, and is forced to rise over the top of it. A region of warm air originating around the Equator will be less dense than one of cold air originating around the Pole. Two such 'air masses', as they are known, will often collide somewhere between the Equator and the Pole, resulting in the lighter, warmer air being pushed up over the heavier, colder air. This is how the whole sky can become covered with cloud. A similar effect happens when wind from one direction encounters wind from another and the only way for the converging air to go is up.

But rising isn't the only way that air can cool enough to form cloud. It can also do so just by mixing with other, colder air. This is what leads to 'contrails', the man-made lines of cloud that form in the exhaust of aircraft up at cruising altitude, which produced the smoking chimney on p88. The water vapour that forms part of the plane's exhaust cools down rapidly as it mixes with the very cold air up at 35,000ft. If the air is cold enough and contains enough water vapour, the exhaust water forms into ice crystals that linger as a line of cloud in the plane's wake.

Cooling by mixing also plays a part in the lowest type of cloud: fog. This can form during a long, clear night when, in the absence of an insulating blanket of cloud in the sky

Air cools to form clouds when:

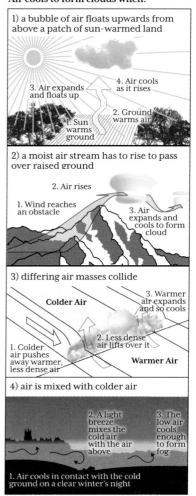

1) a bubble of air floats upwards from above a patch of sun-warmed land

3. Air expands and floats up
4. Air cools as it rises
2. Ground warms air
1. Sun warms ground

2) a moist air stream has to rise to pass over raised ground

2. Air rises
1. Wind reaches an obstacle
3. Air expands and cools to form cloud

3) differing air masses collide

Colder Air
3. Warmer air expands and so cools
2. Less dense air lifts over it
1. Colder air pushes away warmer, less dense air
Warmer Air

4) air is mixed with colder air

2. A light breeze mixes the cold air with the air above
3. The low air cools enough to form fog
1. Air cools in contact with the cold ground on a clear winter's night

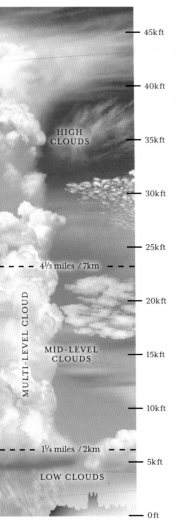

45kft

40kft

HIGH
CLOUDS — 35kft

30kft

25kft

- - - - 4⅓ miles / 7km - - - -

20kft

MID-LEVEL
CLOUDS — 15kft

10kft

- - - - 1¼ miles / 2km - - - -

5kft

LOW CLOUDS

0ft

above, the ground cools rapidly as it radiates the day's heat into the sky, and so cools the air in contact with it. But fog forms in this way only when there is also a slight breeze to stir the air up. This mixes air cooled by the ground with warmer air a few feet above. As they mix, the lowest layer of air can cool sufficiently for some of its water vapour to condense into droplets, making a shallow fog.

The main factor in determining the shape and form of clouds when they do appear is how winds vary from one region to the next and at different altitudes. Winds also determine the way large storm systems develop and move.

Unlikely as it may sound, dirt is an essential ingredient in the formation of most clouds. Microscopic airborne particles, such as tiny crystals of sea salt, dust, volcanic ash or smoke particles, act as little seeds on to which water droplets can begin to form or ice crystals freeze. Although we can't generally see these tiny 'nuclei', typically the air is full of them, which is just as well for without them we'd have barely any clouds at all.

How high are clouds?

If the lowest cloud, fog, is down at ground level, what about the others? Almost all clouds form in a region known as the 'troposphere'. This is the lower eight miles (42,000ft, 12km) or so of our atmosphere (although the actual height of the troposphere varies around the world). It contains most of the atmosphere's water vapour, and is where our weather happens.

Low clouds like the boxers on p42 tend to have bases somewhere below 6,500ft (1¼ miles, 2km). Mid-level clouds like the goggle-eyed UFO on p89 tend to have bases somewhere between 6,500 and 23,000ft (1¼–4⅓ miles, 2–7km). High clouds like the cloud having a bad-hair day on p54 tend to be somewhere between 16,500 and 45,000ft (3–8½ miles, 5–14km). The tallest is the Cumulonimbus storm cloud, like the cloud having a bad-hair-and-big-nose day on p58, which can extend right up through the troposphere and sometimes a bit beyond. The very largest ones might reach from 1,000ft (⅕ mile, 300m) up to as high as 65,000ft (12 miles, 20km) – twice the height of Mount Everest.

Then there are a couple of special cloud types that occur much higher in the atmosphere than any of the weather clouds. The bird of paradise on p20 is a nacreous cloud, which forms just within the stratosphere, the next step above the troposphere, at altitudes of between 10 and 15 miles (49,000–82,000ft, 15–25km). Noctilucent clouds, like the rippled cloud in the background behind the hovering bee on p24, are the highest known clouds in our atmosphere. They form in the 'mesosphere', the next region up, even beyond the stratosphere, at altitudes of around 50 miles (80km) or so.

What's with the funny names?

Two hundred years or so ago, when weather observers first proposed classifying clouds, Englishman Luke Howard suggested giving them Latin names like the scientific names for plants and animals. The argument went that if their names were in a universal language, weather observers around the world would be more likely to stick with them rather than translate them into their own languages, and this would make it easier to share observations of the sky from one region to another.

Finding shapes in the clouds might seem a long way from scientific classification, but many of the Latin names for clouds are simply based on what they look like. Cumulus clouds, like the polar bear in sunglasses on p32, are named after the Latin for a 'stack' or 'heap', since they look like piled up heaps of cloud. Cirrus clouds, like the giant eel on p18, are named after the Latin for a 'lock of hair'. Stratus clouds, like the one forming into a waterfall on p49, get their name from the Latin for a 'sheet' or 'cover', since they are flat, extended layers of cloud.

The names are also determined by how high the clouds are. The names of clouds in the mid-level regions of the troposphere begin with Alto, the same word used in music for a singing part in the middle range. Altocumulus is a mid-level cloud made up of clumps; Altostratus is a mid-level layer. The high clouds, in addition to Cirrus, have names that start with Cirro: Cirrocumulus for high clumps, Cirrostratus for high layers.

Clouds that always precipitate, whether with rain, snow or hail, have names that contain 'nimbus'. Cumulonimbus is the huge storm cloud, often shaped like an anvil, that produces heavy and short-lived showers. Nimbostratus is the thick, grey blanket cloud that produces steady and prolonged rain or snow.

The Ten Main Cloud Types

Low clouds
1. Cumulus (individual clumps, the 'fair-weather' cloud)
2. Stratocumulus (a layer that is composed of clumps)
3. Stratus (a featureless blanket, can form at ground level)

Mid-level clouds
4. Altocumulus (clumps, either individual or in a layer)
5. Altostratus (a featureless blanket, 'the boring cloud')

High clouds
6. Cirrus (translucent, wavy streaks)
7. Cirrocumulus (a layer of clumps, usually as patches, rarely across the whole sky, so high that they appear like grains)
8. Cirrostratus (a translucent, featureless blanket)

Multi-level clouds
9. Cumulonimbus (mountainous storm cloud, sometimes in the shape of an anvil when distant, produces heavy showers)
10. Nimbostratus (thick, grey, featureless blanket, produces prolonged and continuous rain or snow)

The Official Classifications

'Shaped like a leaping dolphin' is not a very helpful description for meteorologists. For this reason, and to sound more grown-up, meteorologists use Latin names for clouds. For those who like to do things the official way, here are the proper classifications for the clouds with their page numbers.

12 Cumulus congestus, with the anvil of a Cumulonimbus storm cloud in the background.

13 Cumulus congestus.

14 Altocumulus with virga (in shadow).

15 Altocumulus with virga.

16 (left) Iridescent colours as the sunlight shines through a patch of ice-crystals produced by an aircraft contrail, with another contrail and Cirrostratus fibratus in the background.

16 (right) Cumulus fractus.

17 Altocumulus, with the light from the sun producing a corona as it is diffracted when it passes around the cloud particles.

18 Cirrus.

19 Cumulus, with a layer of Altostratus visible in the background.

20 Nacreous, also known as polar stratospheric clouds and mother-of-pearl clouds on account of the way the ice crystals diffract the sunlight to produce iridescent colours.

21 Altocumulus lenticularis.

22 Cumulus (in shadow), with some light Cirrostratus in the background.

23 Altocumulus lenticularis.

24 A patch of Altocumulus (in shadow) in the shape of the bee, with noctilucent clouds in the background.

25 (left) Cumulus congestus.

25 (right) Cumulus fractus (the horse), with Cumulus and Stratocumulus below.

26 Cumulus.

27 Cumulus.

28 Cumulus congestus, with the distant anvil of a Cumulonimbus storm cloud in the background.

29 Cumulus congestus.

30 Cirrus (the hound) and Cumulus (from which it's jumping).

31 Altocumulus with virga.

32 Cumulus.

33 Cumulus congestus, with Cirrostratus and an aircraft contrail in the background.

34 Cumulus, with some Cirrus and small patches of Altocumulus lenticularis in the background.

35 Altocumulus with virga, coloured by the evening light.

38 Cumulus.

39 Cumulus and Stratocumulus, with Altostratus in the background.

40 Altocumulus lenticularis.

41 Cumulus.
42 Cumulus congestus.
43 Cumulus.
43 Altocumulus.
44 Towering Cumulus.
45 Lightning from Cumulonimbus (which is viewed from below).
46 Cirrus.
47 Cirrus (in the evening light).
48 Kelvin-Helmholtz wave cloud.
49 Stratus.
50 (left) Aircraft contrails, with Cirrostratus in the background.
50 (right) Cumulus.
51 Cumulonimbus and Cumulus congestus, with Altocumulus and Altostratus in the background.
54 Cirrus.
55 Cumulus congestus.
56 (left) Cumulus.
56 (right) Cumulus congestus with pileus cloud forming over its summit.
57 Cumulonimbus calvus.
58 Cumulonimbus capillatus.
59 Cumulonimbus capillatus.
62 Cumulonimbus.
63 Altocumulus, with Cirrostratus in the background.
64 Cumulonimbus casting a shadow on to a layer of

Altocumulus, showing in the background.
65 Cumulus, with Cirrostratus in the background.
66 Cumulonimbus calvus.
67 Altocumulus lenticularis, cap cloud and Cumulus (in shadow).
68 Cumulus and Cumulus fractus.
69 Mamma formations, also known as mammatus, on the underside of an arcus, or shelf cloud, extending at the front of the base of a Cumulonimbus storm cloud.
70 Altocumulus lenticularis, with Cirrostratus and aircraft contrails in the background.
71 Cumulus.
72 Cumulonimbus calvus.
73 Cumulus, with Altostratus in the background.
76 Cumulus fractus.
77 Aircraft contrails and Cirrus.
78 Cirrus.
79 Cumulus.
80 Altocumulus stratiformis.
81 Cumulus (in shadow) with Cirrus in the background.
82 Aircraft contrail casting a shadow on to Cirrostratus.
83 Aircraft contrail (passing behind the mountain) and faint

banner cloud (on the side of the mountain).
84 Cap cloud.
85 Horseshoe vortex cloud and Cumulus fractus.
86 Cumulonimbus (from below).
87 Cumulus with Cirrus in the background.
88 Aircraft contrail.
89 Altocumulus lenticularis.
90 Pannus, within the precipitation below a Cumulonimbus.
91 Cirrus that has developed from an aircraft contrail, with patches of Cirrocumulus in the background.
92 Cumulus fractus.
93 Altocumulus, with Cirrus in the background.
94 Cumulus fractus.
95 Cumulus, with the anvil of a distant Cumulonimbus in the background.
96 Altocumulus, with Altostratus in the background.
97 Cumulus and Stratocumulus, with crepuscular rays visible below.
98 Cumulus, with Altostratus in the background.
99 Cumulus, with Cirrus in the background.

Acknowledgements

I am grateful to all the members of, and visitors to, The Cloud Appreciation Society who have sent in their photographs of clouds that look like things for our online Cloud Gallery. Of course, I am particularly thankful to those who agreed to their images being included in this collection – both to the members, listed opposite, whose images ended up in the book and also, just as importantly, to those whose wonderful photographs, for one reason or another, did not make our final selection. In places, we changed the description of the cloud from the photographer's original one, when we felt it would make the images work better together. We hope that the contributors forgive us these reinterpretations. We realise that one person's 'question mark' is another person's 'seahorse'; one person's 'Alfred Hitchcock', another person's 'Cee Lo Green'.

I am also very grateful to the two people who found time in their busy schedules to comment on the science pages at the back of the book: Giles Harrison, Professor of Atmospheric Physics at Reading University (and C.A.S. Member 1,506), and Stephen Burt, Fellow of The Royal Meteorological Society (and C.A.S. Member 2,814). Both gave extremely helpful and constructive criticism, and assisted by spotting errors. Thank you as well to Ian Loxley and Sheena Russell for their help in the process of selecting images and contacting members, to Carole Welch, my editor at Sceptre, Lucy Foster and, as always, to my agent Patrick Walsh.

Index of Photographers

Adam, John A 40
Albiston, Jordie 16
Anderson, Megan L 23
Beardsley, Peter.....................70
Bethell, Thomas J 64
Beyne, Eric 90
Bleeker, Keimpe.....................86
Carbone, Modestino 78, 80
Cerutti, Gianni 49
Cliff, Alex 45, 73
Cordelli, Pietro 28
Coutts, Rowena.....................50
de Robeck, Melissa 85
Dent, Marie.......................... 48
Desforges, Jane 55
Dixon-Rowland, Jeanne 25
Downie, Anne 62
Dowson, Gregory 69
Fairclough, Gareth 31
Filippidis, Lazaros 51
Flockton, Mandy Millie 59
Forsdike, Ian 12
Gledhill, Steve.......................96
Good, Adele 99
Gray, John 92
Harrison, Gail J 34

Hart, Elizabeth 38
Hemsworth, Mary 84
Hodgson, Donald Macleod.....50
Holbrooke, David R...............14
Huhtakangas, Tiina 56
Iacono, Fiorella 26
Janes, Jules 94
Johannesen, Carolyn............. 77
Jones, Paul A..........................47
Kaliner, Bernhard 88
Kehl, Michael 93
Kirby, Howard 30
Kirk, Andrew 21
Lantman, Nienke 65
Le Blancq, Frank 18
Leyland, Phil 33
Light, Zan.............................. 72
Lloyd, Karen M 97
Loebig, Paul 46
Lofting, Nikki 27
Loxley, Ian 35, 58
Marr, Rebecca 22
Matthews, Patricia........... 42, 67
McDonald, Moragh 54
Mekhneche, Julien 56, 98
Menger, Michael 71

Milyovsky, Barry....................17
Montgomerie, Lee..................20
Murphy, Maartje and Owain ..25
Murray, Mark 87
Nüchtern, Klaus.....................76
Osanga, Cobalt.......................89
Rowell, Peter 63
Rowlands, John 39
Shaw, Sue 41, 68
Siebenhaar, Danièle 43
Solomon, Andrew 83
Tack, Jason 82
Taylor, Doug.......................... 81
Thomassen, Alan....................43
Tobin, Gavin 19
Tondelier, Laurence 79
Tough, Alan C................. 16, 24
Tremain, Cathryn 91
van der Sluis, Saskia 13
Ward, Ellen Claire 15
Westmaas, Ron...................... 44
Williams, Jeremy 29
Williamson, Bill.....................32
Wilson, Catherine Strong.......66
Wright, Gordon 57
Yap, Tracey............................95

Captions Index

Air guitar performance over Isle of Harris, Scotland **50**

Aircraft *see* 'Cleared for takeoff'

Angry neighbour over Catcott, Somerset, UK **44**

Arrow *see* 'You are here' *and* 'Hang gliders, turn right here'

Bad-hair day:
  a big one taken in the 1950s, over Newton-on-Ouse, North Yorkshire, UK **57**
  a comb-over one, over Pori, Finland **56**
  and big-nose day over Upton, Lincolnshire, UK **58**
  over Boston, Lincolnshire, UK **55**
  over Cullen, Moray, Scotland **54**
  over Montpellier, France **56**
  Santa's, over St Ives, Cornwall, UK **59**

Ballet dancers warming up over Burton Bradstock, Dorset, UK **46**

Bee hovering in the shadows over Elgin, Moray, Scotland **24**

Bird:
  cockerel, over Bishop, California, US **21**
  of paradise over Leeds, UK **20**
  also see Swan

Bodybuilder flexing his muscles over Pacifica, California, US **47**

Boxing practice in the park over Weed, California, US **42**

Bunny *see* Rabbit

Chimney, smoking, over Munich, Germany **88**

'Cleared for takeoff' over Norwich, Norfolk, UK **81**

Dog:
  puppy begging for dinner over Manchester, UK **33**
  suicidal Afghan Hound over Wigmore, Herefordshire, UK **30**

Dolphin, leaping over Sausalito, California, US **14**

Dragon landing on the Isle of Skye, Scotland **94**

Elephant:
  baby, over Bedford, Bedfordshire, UK **12**
  mummy, over Terschelling, The Netherlands **13**

Face *see* Sunny face

Feather *see* Quill

Fish:
  giant eel over Ouaisné Bay, St Brelade, Jersey, UK **18**
  rainbow, caught in a net over Elgin, Moray, Scotland **16**
  red snapper over The Blasket Islands, County Kerry, Ireland **19**
  seahorse over Eltham, Victoria, Australia **16**
  sunfish over Big Bend National Park, Texas, US **17**

Flying saucer *see* UFO

Frisbee thrower over Banff, Alberta, Canada **40**

Ghost carrying home the shopping over Aberdeen, Scotland **87**

Giant sniffing a row of herbs over Grou, Friesland, The Netherlands **86**

Gorilla and hippopotamus over Stockgrove Country Park, Leighton Buzzard, UK **29**

Grumpy old man from The Muppet Show over Bangkok, Thailand **73**

Guitarist *see* Air guitar

Hamlet with Yorick's skull over South Yearle, Northumberland, UK **68**

Hand *see* 'Talk to the hand' *and* Thumbs up

'Hang gliders, turn right here' over Melbourne, Australia **50**

Hat *see* Mother-in-law's *and* Musketeer

Heart:
  broken, over Montpellier, France **98**
  mended, over Sedona, Arizona, US **99**

Hippopotamus *see* Gorilla and hippopotamus

Hitchcock, Alfred, watching a storm over Ecclefechan, Scotland **62**

Holmes, Sherlock, over Kalkan, Turkey **71**

Horse leaping over Hyde, Cheshire, UK **25**

Jagger, Mick, lips, over Sherwood Rise, Nottingham, UK **70**

Jesus over Christchurch, New Zealand **69**

Lightning Boy climbing on the wires over Bangkok, Thailand **45**

Lovers having a cuddle over Zurich, Switzerland **43**

Missile strikes, accidental:
  over Houston, Texas, US **82**
  over the Matterhorn, on the Italian-Swiss border **83**

Mother-in-law's:
  walking stick over Naas, County Kildare, Ireland **85**
  wedding hat on top of Lion's Head mountain, Cape Town, South Africa **84**

Murray, Andy, serving an ace over Traigh Beach, Arisaig, Scotland **63**

Musketeer:
  Aramis over Ann Arbor, Michigan, US **64**
  Athos over Loudonville, Ohio, US **66**
  d'Artagnan over Erm, The Netherlands **65**
  feathered hat over Mount Shasta, California, US **67**

Neighbour *see* Angry neighbour

Numbers:
  'FIVE' over Vienna, Austria **76**
  'FOUR' over Welling, Kent, UK **77**
  'ONE' over Mercogliano, Italy **80**
  'THREE' over Naples, Italy **78**
  'TWO' over Drumnadrochit, Inverness, Scotland **79**

Pig's head over Finchley, North London, UK **27**

Polar bear in shades taking a stroll along Bamburgh Beach, Northumberland, UK **32**

Potter, Harry, scar over Bishop, California, US **90**

Question mark over Steinenbronn, Germany **93**

Quill over Jamieson, Victoria, Australia **91**

Rabbit:
  fat one, doing gymnastics over Modena, Italy **26**
  looking up over Friesland, The Netherlands **25**

Rat, giant, telling a secret over Tortona, Alessandria, Italy **28**

Rowers over South Leigh, Oxfordshire, UK **48**

Shark patrolling the road from Marrakesh to Agadir, Morocco **15**

Simpson, Homer, befriends a
    squirrel over Cardiff, South
    Wales, UK 72
Sunbather, topless, over Wooler,
    Northumberland, UK 41
Sunny face over Porthcawl,
    Wales, UK 97
Surfer, kneeling over Sabden,
    Lancashire, UK 38
Swan:
    swimming over Colorado
        Springs, Colorado, US 34
    taking off over Upton,
        Lincolnshire, UK 35
Swimmer waving from the
    surf over Malltraeth,
    Anglesey, UK 39
'Talk to the hand' over Chadbury,
    Worcestershire, UK 96
Tennis player *see* Murray, Andy
Thumbs up over Istanbul,
    Turkey 51
Tree over Bexhill-on-Sea, East
    Sussex, UK 43
Tyrannosaurus Rex:
    baby, over Orkney, Scotland 22
    grown-up, over Friesland, The
        Netherlands 23
UFO, goggle-eyed, over the
    Devils Marbles, Northern
    Territory, Australia 89
Walking stick *see* Mother-in-law's

Waterfall over Geneva,
    Switzerland 49
Witch taking off over Marsiling,
    Singapore 95
Wolf howling over Winter Hill,
    Bolton, UK 31
'You are here' over Milford
    Sound, New Zealand 92